Busy Bee
Make and Do

 Make and Do activities that require adult supervision are marked with this

Illustrated by
Helen Prole and Claire Philpott

Designed and produced by
Autumn Publishing Ltd
Chichester, West Sussex, PO20 7EQ, UK

© 2005 Autumn Publishing Ltd

Printed in China

ISBN 1 84531 306 2

BYEWAY
B O O K S

Colourful Butterflies

These brightly coloured butterflies will brighten up any room. They are simple and easy to make. Make butterflies of all sizes to decorate the walls and windows of your bedroom.

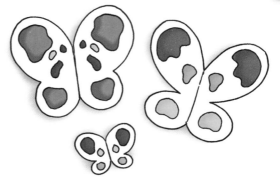

1 Cover your work surface with old newspaper. Mix some paint in a mixing tray, keeping the colours separate.

2 Fold a sheet of white paper in half. Keeping the paper folded, draw one side of a butterfly and cut it out carefully.

3 Open the butterfly and drip some paints on to one half. Re-fold the butterfly and press down firmly with fingertips.

4 Unfold the butterfly and leave to dry. Ask an adult to help you stick the colourful butterfly on a wall or window.

old newspapers   paint   mixing tray   white paper   pencil   scissors

Potato Printing

A fun and easy way to make your own wrapping paper and greeting card designs. Try using different shapes to make different patterns. Surprise your friends or family with a hand printed card.

1 Choose a shape to print. Make it simple, like a heart, flower or star. Get an adult to cut a potato in half to make a flat surface.

2 Draw the shape you want on one face of the potato. Get an adult to cut around the shape, leaving the shape raised.

3 Dry the potato on some kitchen roll. Paint over the raised shape. Press down on the paper and hold in place for a few seconds.

4 Carefully take the potato away and make more prints. Try different colours to make a pattern. Allow to dry.

potato

pencil

knife

kitchen roll

paint

white paper or card

Cress Seed Fun

A deliciously fun way to grow your own cress. Grow the cress in the shape of a letter. It could be the first letter of your name! Check every day to see how much the cress has grown. When fully-sprouted, you can eat it!

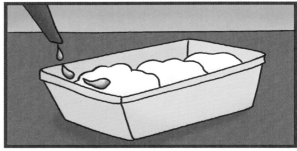

1 Cover the bottom of a margarine tub with cotton wool or kitchen roll. Soak the cotton wool/kitchen roll with water.

2 Shake some cress seeds onto the wet cotton wool/kitchen roll in the shape of the letter you want. You may need to ask an adult to help.

3 Put the tub next to a sunny window and make sure you keep the cotton wool/kitchen roll wet. Check the growth each day.

4 The cress should be fully grown in a week. Cut the cress close to the bottom of the stalks. Wash and use in a salad or sandwich.

empty margarine tub

cotton wool or kitchen roll

watering can

cress seeds

scissors

Brilliant Badges!

Make these great badges for you and your friends to wear. You can make them as colourful or as sparkly as you want. You can also attach them to birthday cards to give to your friends and family. You can make picture or name badges in the same way.

1 Draw a letter or number on a piece of card. Don't make it too big!

2 Cut out the letter or number and decorate it using your brightest colours. Add some glitter to make it sparkle!

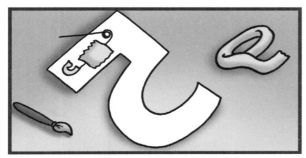

3 When the letter or number is decorated, carefully tape a safety pin to the back of it. Ask an adult for help when you do this.

4 If you want to attach the badge to a card, pin it to the front. This is tricky so you may need some help from an adult.

plain or coloured card

scissors

safety pin

glitter

paints and pencils

glue and sticky tape

Collage Picture

This is a fun and very easy project to do. To prepare for it you will need to collect lots of different things, such as feathers, shells, string, ribbons, old magazine pictures, dry pasta shapes, etc. Make a picture using as many things as you can!

1 Look at the items you have collected and decide what sort of picture you want to make.

2 To make a beach scene, spread some glue along the bottom of the paper and sprinkle on some sand.

3 Paint on a sky and use your collected items to make the picture. Add shells and use cotton wool for clouds.

4 When the collage is finished, frame your picture with some strong card and get an adult to help hang it on a wall.

collected bits and pieces

paper or card

glue

glue brush

scissors

Growing Beans

Show everyone what green fingers you have by growing runner beans in a jar. Make a chart to record how quickly your beans grow. Don´t forget to plant them in your garden when they start to grow really big!

1 Put an empty yoghurt pot upside down in a jar. Roll some blotting paper into a tube and place it over the yoghurt pot.

2 Place 3 or 4 runner beans between the blotting paper and the jar. Make sure they are wedged against the inside of the jar.

3 Fill the jar a quarter full of water. Put the jar in a warm, sunny place.

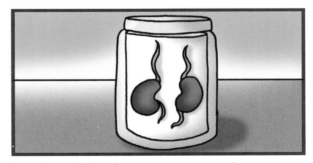

4 Look at the beans every day to see how they have grown. Add more water so that the blotting paper doesn't dry out.

empty yoghurt pot

jam jar

blotting paper

runner bean seeds

watering can

Bubble Printing

A simple and messy way to make some exciting prints. You will need a lot of old newspaper to cover the work surface! These prints are great for wrapping paper or make a crazy space-like background for you to draw a picture on. Try it out!

1 Squeeze a generous amount of washing-up liquid into the bowl of water. Swish the water to make lots of frothy bubbles.

2 Cover the work surface with newspaper. Dribble coloured inks or food colourings onto the bubbles – you will need to work quickly!

3 Take a sheet of white paper and lay it gently onto the surface of the bubbles and remove it after a few seconds.

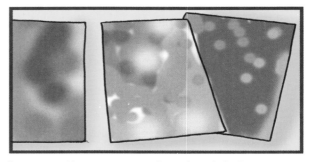

4 Leave the paper to dry. Make another bowl of bubbles, using different colours.

old newspaper

washing-up liquid

washing-up bowl and water

coloured inks or food colourings

white paper

Grow a Hyacinth

Plant a bulb in December and watch and wait for it to blossom into a beautiful hyacinth in spring. Keep a bulb diary in which you can write about and draw pictures of the bulb's growth into a flowering plant.

1 Cover the work surface with plenty of old newspaper. Using a trowel, fill a flowerpot halfway with potting compost.

2 Place a hyacinth bulb in the centre of the compost. Make sure the rounded part of the bulb is at the bottom.

3 Add some more compost around the bulb, leaving about 2cm of the bulb showing above the soil. Stand the pot in a dish of water.

4 Place the pot in a cool, dark place for about eight weeks. Remember to water it. When shoots appear, move it to a warm, light room.

old newspaper

flowerpot

trowel

potting compost

hyacinth bulb

All Aboard!

Take teddy for a ride in his very own train. Attach a string to the engine to make this a pull-along toy train. There's even a lever to move! Move it forwards to speed along the tracks. Move it back to stop at stations along the way. Toot! Toot!

1 Cut one large side out of two cereal boxes. Slot together and join the edges with sticky tape.

2 Draw and colour a picture of a toy animal onto a piece of paper. Tape this to the front of the train.

3 Hold the tube against the train and tape the strip of card over it to make the lever.

4 Cut eight wheels from coloured paper and glue along the sides of the train.

2 cereal boxes

scissors

sticky tape

paper and card

cardboard tube

glue and crayons

Cat Mask

Pretend to be a cat in your very own cat mask. Follow the instructions to turn yourself into a furry feline. Use different coloured card to make lots of different masks.

1 Draw these mask shapes onto some card and cut them out. Ask an adult to help you cut out the eye holes.

2 Glue two pink ears in place. Make sure the glue is dry before starting step 3.

3 Glue some cotton wool in place to look like fur, and stick a pink nose on top.

4 Glue string to the cotton wool to make whiskers. Make holes, as shown, and attach elastic.

card

pencil and glue

scissors

cotton wool

string

elastic

Butterfly Mobile

This mobile is a great way to use the butterflies you made earlier in `Colourful Butterflies´. Hang the mobile near a window and watch the butterflies move in the breeze.

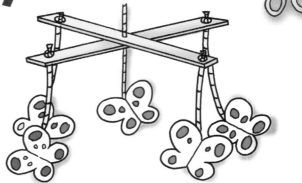

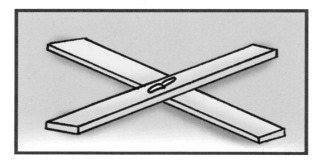

1 Paint two long strips of thick card. Ask an adult to help you find the centres and to insert a split pin to secure them in an 'X' shape.

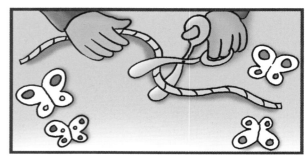

2 Cut five pieces of thread about 20cm long. Tie a knot in the end of each one. Make five butterflies for the mobile.

3 Make a hole in the end of each section of the crossbar. Push the threads through the holes so the knots are at the top.

4 Tape the butterflies to the other end of the threads. Add a thread and butterfly to the centre. Ask an adult to hang it up for you.

paint

2 strips thick card 4cm x 25cm

thread and a split pin

scissors

5 `Colourful butterflies´

sticky tape

Puppy Puppet

An old sock can be transformed into a great puppy puppet. Use socks of all colours to make different animals and characters. Ask a parent to wear the sock while you decorate it.

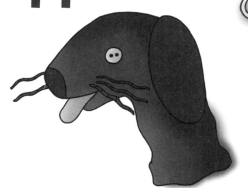

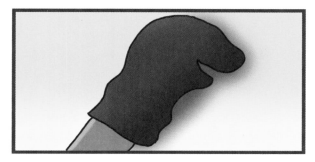

1 Put the sock on a parents' hand with the fingers in the toe part. Push the sock between the thumb and fingers to form the mouth.

2 Glue on two buttons to make the eyes. Make sure they are level! Cut a circle of black felt to make a nose and stick this on.

3 Cut two long oval shapes from the black felt to make the ears. Cut a smaller oval of pink felt to make the tongue and stick on.

4 Cut a few strands of black wool to make the whiskers. Stick these either side of the nose. Make sure the glue has dried before playing with your puppet.

old sock

buttons and black wool

glue

black and pink felt

scissors

Fairy Wings

Turn yourself into a beautiful fairy with these fantastic fairy wings. Make them as colourful and sparkly as you want. They are great to wear to any fancy dress party!

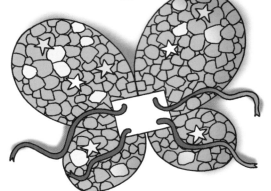

1  On one sheet of card draw a large wing shape. Cut the shape out and turn it over to use as a template to make the other wing.

2  Spread glue on the wings and press on layers of torn tissue paper. Cover both wings. Glue on sequins and glitter.

3 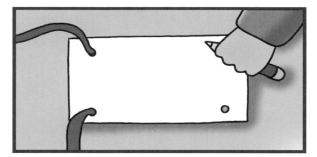 Cut a rectangle of card 15cm wide by 10cm high. Make holes in each corner. Thread and knot the ribbons into the holes.

4 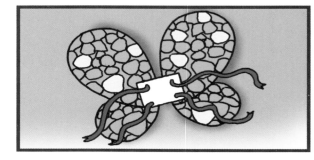 Glue the rectangle to the wings, as shown. The wings should meet in the middle. Leave the wings to dry.

3 large sheets of card

glue and crayon

scissors

coloured tissue paper

glitter and sequins

4 x 40cm lengths of ribbon

Musical Shakers

Make great music with this amazing musical shaker. Use different kinds of dried beans to make different sounds. Play along with your favourite music or get together with friends and form a band.

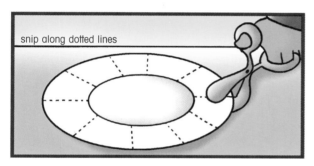

snip along dotted lines

1 Trace the end of the tube onto card. Draw a larger circle around the tracing, and cut it out. Snip along dotted lines. Make two.

2 Spread glue onto the snipped sections of one circle. Glue it to seal one end of the tube.

3 Cut two pieces of kitchen foil one and a half times the length of the tube. Scrunch them into coils and put them into the tube.

4 Pour about a mug full of beans into the tube. Seal the other end of the tube. Decorate the tube with strips of paper or paint it in your favourite colours.

thin card

cardboard tube

scissors

glue and crayon

kitchen foil

small dried beans

Fire Engine Toy Box

Make a fab fire engine to play with. You can pretend you are a brave firefighter with this great truck. When you have finished playing, you can use it to store toys.

1 With the open end of a box upwards, paint the entire box red. You may need to do a couple of coats. Leave to dry.

2 Cut a strip of light blue paper for the windscreen. Make sure it almost covers the width of the box. Glue smaller squares for the sides.

3 Cut two circles of white paper to make the headlights. Glue these to the front of the box. Paint four paper plates black for the wheels.

4 When dry, glue them to the sides of the box. Draw and cut out a ladder, hose, hubcaps and bumper, and stick in place.

cardboard box

black and red paint

coloured paper

scissors

glue

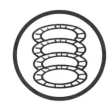

4 paper plates

Super Sail Boat

It only takes a few minutes to make these super sailboats. Make them with your friends and float them in a large container, in the bath or on a pond. Remember: always have an adult with you when playing near water!

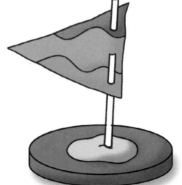

1 Cut a triangle from a piece of coloured paper and decorate it. Make three holes down one edge of the sail with a hole punch.

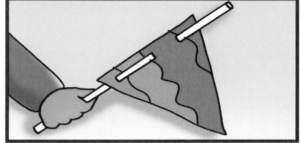

2 Push a drinking straw through the holes in the sail. This will make the boat's mast.

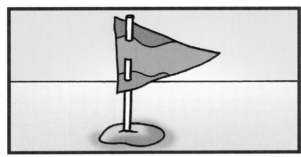

3 Put a small ball of modelling clay in the middle of a plastic lid. Push the end of the straw into the clay to make the mast stand up.

4 Your boat should be ready to sail. If the boat tips over, move the modelling clay until you find the centre and the boat floats.

coloured paper

scissors

hole punch

straight drinking straw

modelling clay

a large plastic lid

Paper Snowflakes

A great way to create a snowy room is to make lots of snowflakes and hang them from the ceiling. Hang them at different lengths to make it look like it is snowing.

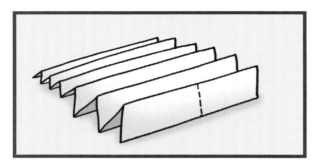

1 With the short edge facing you, concertina fold a sheet of paper until you get to the end of the paper. Fold in half and mark a line.

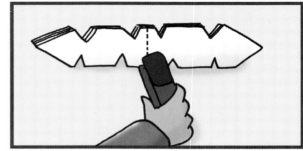

2 Ask an adult to staple along the marked line. With the paper still folded, cut the ends into points. Cut triangular shapes into the edges.

3 Open the concertina out and glue or staple the ends together to make the full snowflake.

4 Spread on glue and glitter. Leave to dry. Attach thread and ask an adult to hang up the snowflake.

white paper

scissors

stapler

glue

glitter

thread

Grow a Sunflower

Growing sunflowers is great fun especially when you have a race with a friend to see who can grow the tallest one. Spring is the best time to plant the seeds. Measure your sunflower's progress, and in the summer you should have a sunflower that towers over you!

1 Start the sunflower off by growing it in a pot. Using a trowel, fill a large flowerpot with potting compost.

2 Push some sunflower seeds into the compost. Plant about six. Cover the seeds with a layer of compost.

3 Water the seeds lightly and keep them in a warm, dry place until the shoots start to appear. Water a little each day.

4 When the plant measures about 5cm, ask an adult to help you plant the sunflower in a sunny part of the garden, near a wall. Keep a look out for snails and slugs!

flowerpot

trowel

potting compost

sunflower seeds

watering can

Egg Box Bugs

Make lots of different bugs to create your own bug collection. Paint the cartons different colours to create different creatures. Use goggly eyes to make the bugs look really funny!

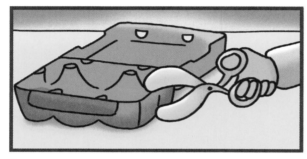

1 Cut out the individual egg cups from an egg box. This may be tricky so ask an adult to help.

2 Paint the egg cups to look like the bug's body. We are using red and black paint for a ladybird. Don't forget to add some spots!

3 Make three holes down each side of the ladybird. Push each pipe cleaner through a hole to the one opposite. Bend the pipe cleaners to form the legs.

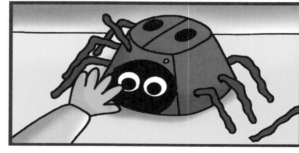

4 Glue on goggly eyes. Make two holes above the eyes. Ask an adult t cut a pipe cleaner in half. Thread th ends of the pipe cleaner through th holes to make the antennae.

egg box

scissors

paints

pipe cleaners

goggly eyes

glue

Sparkly Tiara

Pretend to be a princess with one of these beautiful tiaras. They are very simple to make and will add sparkle to any fashion princess's wardrobe. Bend the foil into different shapes to make interesting patterns.

1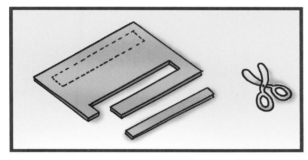

Measure and cut out two strips, about 3cm wide, from a piece of card.

2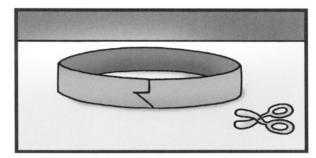

Glue the strips together to make one strip. Fit around your head and ask an adult to cut and glue the strip to the correct size.

3

Cut strips of kitchen foil and twist them into 'sticks'. Bend the foil 'sticks' into heart shapes and glue them to the front of your tiara.

4

Decorate your tiara with glitter and sequins.

shiny or colourful card

sticky tape

scissors

glue

glitter and sequins

kitchen foil

Wiggly Caterpillar

This colourful, wiggly caterpillar is fun and easy to make. Use lots of different coloured paper to make it look very bright or just two colours to make it more stripy. Add some goggly eyes to make Wiggles look really funny!

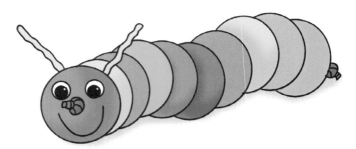

1 Draw round a plastic cup onto card to make a circle. Do this until you have about 20 circles. Cut them out.

2 Poke a hole through each of the circles with the end of a pencil. Ask an adult to help. Make the hole big enough to thread wool or string.

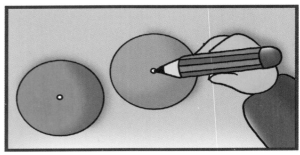

3 Cut a long piece of string and tie a knot in one end. Start threading the coloured circles onto the string.

4 After the last circle, knot the string. Bend a pipe cleaner in half to make antennae. Tape it to the back of the last circle. Draw or glue on eyes and give Wiggles a big smiley mouth.

plastic cup

coloured card

pencil and glue

scissors

string or wool

pipe cleaner

Wizard's Hat

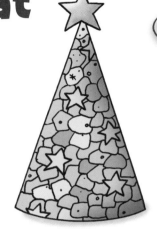

Turn yourself into a wizard with this amazing wizard's hat. Simple to make and very effective, this hat is a great thing to wear to a fancy dress party. Use pink tissue instead of blue to make a princess headdress.

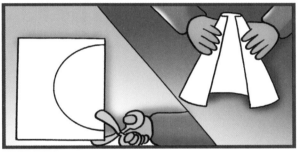

1 Draw a large semicircle on a sheet of white card. It needs to measure 50cm along the straight edge. Fold into a cone shape.

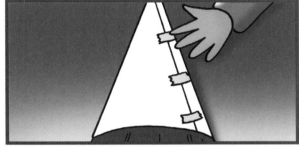

2 Adjust the size of the cone until it fits the head. Secure the join with sticky tape. Ask an adult to help you with steps 1 and 2.

3 Tear different shades of blue tissue paper into small pieces and glue in layers over the cone. Do this until the hat is covered. Leave to dry.

4 Decorate with glitter and stars. Cut two identical stars from card and stick back to back to cover the top of the hat.

large sheet
white card

pencil

sticky tape

blue tissue
paper

glue and
brush

stars and
glitter

Flower Power

Surprise a parent, relative or teacher with a beautiful bunch of handmade flowers. They are simple to make and will last for ever. Ask a parent if you can spray a little perfume on the petals to make the flowers smell like the real thing!

1 Cut out the separate egg cup sections from an egg box. Paint them, inside and out, bright yellow or orange. Leave to dry.

2 Draw lots of large petal shapes onto coloured card and cut them out. You will need up to eight petals for each flower.

3 Dab some glue on the base of the egg cup and stick the petals around it to make the flower. Make sure the petals are evenly spaced.

4 Scrunch yellow tissue paper into a ball and glue it inside the egg cup. Tape a drinking straw to the back of the flower as a stem.

egg box and scissors

coloured card

paints

straight drinking straw

yellow tissue paper

glue or sticky tape

Flower Bonnet

Brighten up a spring day with this lovely flower bonnet. It's simple and quick to make. Decorate it with lots of paper flowers and ribbons to make it look really pretty. Make some bonnets with your friends and have a bonnet parade.

1 Ask an adult to cut four slits across the centre of the plate, starting each slit 3cm from the edge of the plate.

2 Bend the eight triangle sections upwards. Paint the bonnet in your favourite colours. Leave the paint to dry.

3 From coloured card, draw and cut out lots of flowers.

4 Glue the flowers to the triangle sections. Cut a strip of crêpe paper and tie it around the hat.

large paper plate

scissors

paints

coloured card

pencil and glue

crêpe paper

Pop-up Card

Make somebody's day by giving them a great pop-up card. This card template can be used to make any image — from a frog to a scary monster — come to life. All you need is a little imagination!

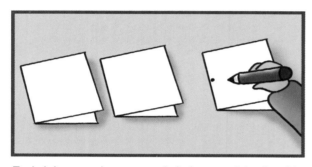

1 Fold two pieces of A4 card in half, as shown here. On one card mark a dot on the folded edge near the middle of the card.

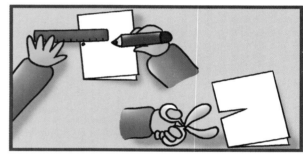

2 Draw and cut a line, 5cm long, from the dot towards the middle of the card. Fold and crease along the cut to form two triangles.

Folded edge of closed card will have triangular indent, as shown above.

3 With the triangles facing upwards, open the card bringing the back of the card to the front. Close the card trapping the open 'mouth' inside.

4 Draw your creature so that the mouth is in the middle of the face. Glue the other card to the back. Decorate the front of your card.

A4 white card

pencil

ruler

scissors

paints

glue

Car Frame

A fun and funky way to display your favourite photos and pictures. Make lots of frames and have a traffic jam of photos, or change the design and make them in different shapes. How about ladybird or snail frames?

1 Fold an A4 sheet of card in half. Make sure the folded edge stays at the top.

2 Draw a car shape with the fold at the top. Cut out the car, but do not cut along the fold.

3 Get an adult to help you cut the photo window out of one side of the car.

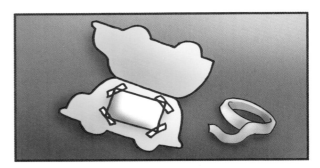

4 Place your photo over the hole so the picture faces out. Use sticky tape to keep the photo in place.

A4 coloured card

pencil

scissors

photo

sticky tape

Piggy Bank

Saving money can be great fun with this fantastic pink piggy bank. This project will take a few days to complete as the papier mâché needs time to dry. You will need an adult to help you with this project. If you don't like pink just paint it in your favourite colours.

1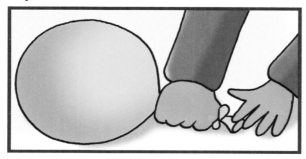

Blow up a balloon to the size of a small melon. Tie a knot in the end. Tear up newspaper into small strips.

2

Make some flour and water glue. Mix 4 cups of flour to 1 cup of water. Dip pieces of newspaper in the glue and layer it onto the balloon.

3

Cover with 2 or 3 layers and leave to dry. Pop the balloon. Cut five egg cup sections from an egg box for the legs and snout. Glue them to the body.

4

Paint the pig pink. Curl the pipe cleaner to make a tail. Tape it to the rear of the pig. Cut triangles of pink paper to make ears. Ask an adult to cut a money slot in the top.

small balloon and eggbox

old newspaper and pink paper

flour and water glue

glue and masking tape

pink paint and pipe cleaner

pencil and felt-tip pen

Magic Wand

Pretend to be a fairy princess or a powerful wizard with this magic wand. Use your imagination to make the wand look pretty and sparkly by using glitter, sequins, beads or kitchen foil.

1 On a sheet of card draw a star shape that measures about 10cm across. Cut the star out and use it as a template to draw another star.

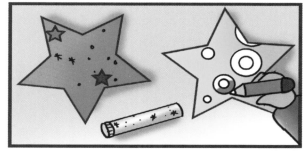

2 Decorate one side of each star with sequins and glitter to make it look really pretty. Remember the stars will be glued together later.

3 Spread glue on the back of one star and stick a dowel rod in the middle. Cut strips of ribbon or tissue paper and glue them along the bottom edge of the star.

4 Spread glue on the back of the remaining star and press the two stars together, back to back. Place a piece of paper and a heavy book on the wand until the glue is dry.

thick white card

scissors

glue and pencil

glitter and sequins

dowel rod or blunt wooden skewer

ribbon or tissue paper

King's Crown

Turn yourself into a king or queen with this brilliant crown. Make it look realistic by adding fake gem stones or silver kitchen foil. Wear it with a long red cloak and you will be a wow at any costume party!

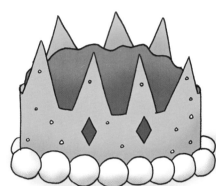

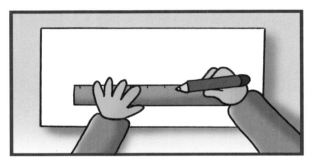

1 Cut out a strip of card 15cm wide and long enough to fit around the head. Allow extra to overlap the ends.

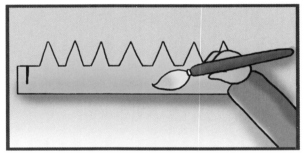

2 Along one long edge, draw a zigzag pattern. Cut it out. If you are using plain card, paint the card gold or silver.

3 Overlap the ends and tape together to make the crown. Glue cotton wool balls along the bottom edge.

4 Cut a large circle from tissue paper. Push inside the crown and tape into place as shown. Decorate the crown with fake gems.

shiny or plain card

ruler and pencil

cotton wool balls

glue and sticky tape

red tissue paper

scissors

Cat Bookmark

Now there is no reason to lose your place in a book ever again! This cute character will hold on to your page until you open the book to read. Very simple and quick to make, you will want to make one for all of your books!

1 Draw the cat shape on a large piece of card.

2 Colour the cat in your favourite colours.

3 Cut the cat out, snipping under the arms. The arms will hold your page.

4 Place the cat bookmark in your book at the right page. Position the paws over the page to hold your place.

white card

pencil

scissors

colouring pencils

glue

Paper Windmills

Make some colourful paper windmills to brighten up a breezy day. Use lots of different coloured paper, including shiny paper and glitter to really make them sparkle as they turn.

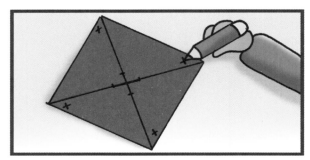

1 Draw lines on the paper, corner to corner, to make a cross. Measure 2cm from the centre along each line and mark with a pencil.

2 Draw a small cross in the left corner of each triangle section. Cut along the lines but stop at the pencil marks.

3 Decorate the windmill with glitter. Bend one corner marked with a cross to the centre point and stick with a little glue. Do this for every corner.

4 Ask an adult to push a pin through the centre of the windmill and through a straw. Secure the pin with a cork, as shown.

coloured paper 14cm X 14cm

ruler and pencil

glitter

scissors and glue

straight drinking straw

cork and mapping pin